mac 2002

Cartoons from the *Daily Mail*

Stan McMurtry **mac**
Edited by Mark Bryant

ROBSON BOOKS

For Nick, Katie and Megan

First published in Great Britain in 2002 by Robson Books,
64 Brewery Road, London N7 9NT

A member of **Chrysalis** Books plc

British Library Cataloguing in Publication Data
A catalogue record for this title is available from the British Library

ISBN 1 86105 549 8

Typeset by SX Composing DTP, Rayleigh, Essex
Printed in Great Britain by St. Edmundsbury Press, Bury St Edmunds, Suffolk

US-led forces bombed Taliban bases in Afghanistan, believed to be harbouring Osama Bin Laden, chief suspect for the 11 September terrorist attacks in the US. Meanwhile, Railtrack went into receivership, to the dismay of its 250,000 shareholders.

'O Holy One. I bring terrible news about your Railtrack shares.'   *9 October 2001*

An outbreak of the killer virus anthrax in Boca Raton, Florida – the first case in 25 years – was blamed on US-based members of Osama Bin Laden's Al Qaeda network who were believed to have stockpiled chemical and biological weapons.

'Well, I think we should have just cancelled the holiday.' *11 October*

President Bush released to the press photographs of the FBI's '22 Most Wanted Terrorists'
Top of the list was Osama Bin Laden but a notable omission was US *bête noir*
President Saddam Hussein of Iraq.

'34th? Oh, come on. Please tell him he's done better than that.' *12 October*

Passenger figures on airlines after the 11 September attacks reached an all-time low when a spokesman for Osama Bin Laden warned Muslims in the US and Britain to avoid air travel and high-rise buildings, suggesting further attacks were imminent.

'He's got the pilot worried – we're on the M4.' *15 October*

As anthrax cases in the US rose to 12 the British government revealed that it only had enough stock of the anti-anthrax drug doxycycline to treat two million people.

'Don't drink that one, mother. It's our anti-anthrax vaccine.' *16 October*

As the war in Afghanistan continued, Home Secretary David Blunkett announced plans for a network of secure 'accommodation centres' to prevent asylum-seekers – many of whom would be subsequently deported – working illegally in Britain.

'Apparently we get three meals a day, a nice uniform and a gun and then get sent someplace where we'll feel completely at home.' *30 October*

An appeal court decided that Tony Martin, the 56-year-old Norfolk farmer convicted of killing a teenage burglar, should serve a further year in prison. Meanwhile, the burglar's accomplice walked free after serving only part of his three-year sentence.

'Good evening, sir. These gentlemen are here to ransack your house. I must warn you that any attempt by you to resist entry could result in a long prison sentence . . .' *1 November*

In the wake of the 11 September hijackings, British Airways and Virgin Atlantic announced that they would be stepping up the security on all their aircraft and installing £1-million bullet-proof cockpit doors to deter terrorists.

'Okay, Captain. We're locked in. Nobody can enter. You can relax . . . Has anyone ever told you what beautiful eyes you've got?' *2 November*

Soon after taking office as the new Speaker of the House of Commons, Glaswegian Michael Martin – former union official 'Gorbals Mick' – was accused of sacking his predecessor's Diary Secretary for being 'too posh'.

'Enunciate, woman, enunciate! You have to impress the man. Now, try again . . . "Gissa job, Jimmy, or ah'll heed butt yer teeth oot!"' *5 November*

Prime Minister Tony Blair's reforms for the House of Lords revealed that only a fifth of the members of the new chamber would be directly elected by the people, the rest being appointed either by their parties or by an independent commission.

'We're very united now. Some of us are elected by Tony, some are appointed and the rest are given frontal lobotomies.' *8 November*

Beleaguered Transport Secretary Stephen Byers was accused of lying to the House of Commons over allegations that he had tried to threaten the independent Rail Regulator. Meanwhile, a study published in *Nature* revealed that sheep have a strong memory for faces.

'I'm sure you're wrong. Stephen Byers' nose is much shorter than that.'   *9 November*

After it was revealed that some of the Arab hijackers behind the 11 September atrocities in the US had links to Britain, Home Secretary David Blunkett introduced emergency powers to imprison suspected international terrorists without trial.

'But she always wears a towel on her head after she's washed her hair!' *12 November*

As a State of Emergency was declared in Britain, veterans of the First and Second World Wars commemorated Remembrance Sunday, which fell on the 11th day of the 11th month for the first time in 11 years.

'**Look, mate. This is where we came during the last lot and we're not leaving till the all-clear.**' *13 November*

As US-led forces captured Afghanistan's capital, Kabul, and local inhabitants liberated from the strict fundamentalist Taliban regime shaved off their beards and played pop music, there was speculation about what other influences the Americans would bring.

'How should we prepare ourselves, O Wise One? What plans do you think the Americans have for our country?'   *15 November*

With the end of five years' rule by the Taliban fundamentalist Muslim regime in Afghanistan, it was decreed that it was no longer compulsory for women to wear the *burqa*, a long enveloping garment that hides their features.

'Remember sensuous, sexy, Fatima the belly dancer, lads? Well, after five years she's back and the *burqa* is off!' *16 November*

As US-led forces closed in on the last remaining pockets of Taliban resistance in the mountains on the border with Pakistan, *Harry Potter and the Philosopher's Stone* – a film of the book about a boy who practices witchcraft – broke all box-office records.

'You see? More lies by the Western infidels. It doesn't work!'   *19 November*

Men and childless women were angered when a tribunal considering the case of a policewoman who wanted to work only daytime shifts, to allow her children to go to nursery school, ruled that any woman with young children had a legal right to refuse early, late or night shiftwork.

'I see the girls have gone home early again to look after their kids.' *20 November*

After eight years' debate and despite strong resistance by local residents and environmental pressure groups, Transport Secretary Stephen Byers gave the go-ahead for the building of a fifth terminal at London's Heathrow Airport.

'I said, great news, Mrs Vaughan. We've had an offer for your house – five quid.' *22 November*

A damning report by Professor David Begg, Chairman of the government's chief transport advisers, the Commission for Integrated Transport, revealed that Britain had the most severe traffic congestion and the highest public transport fares in Europe.

'If we're still here at Christmas, me and the driver was wondering if you'd like to pop in for a drink?' *26 November*

In a day of visits to celebrate the achievements of the broadcasting industry, the Queen and Prince Philip visited ITN, CNN, the BBC World Service and the set of the TV soap *EastEnders* at Elstree Studios in Hertfordshire.

'Stone me, Benskin. We've been goin' round the bleedin' TV studios all day and we're knackered. Pour us a couple of pints and 'ave one yourself.' *29 November*

In an attempt to deter drink-drivers at Christmas, Thames Valley Police offered up to £500 to members of the public who rang a confidential phone number to report on friends, neighbours and even family members who drove when over the limit.

'Goodnight. Lovely to see you all. Safe journey home . . . Hello, police? They're just leaving . . .' *30 November*

A group of 12 British planespotters on a package holiday in Greece were arrested and faced sentences of up to 20 years in prison for espionage.

'Guards, quickly! There's someone looking at our aeroplane!' *3 December*

Sleaze watchdog, Elizabeth Filkin, who had been appointed as Parliamentary Commissioner for Standards in 1999, resigned after claiming that she had been the victim of a smear campaign and had been obstructed while trying to carry out her job.

'Of course, this is only until we've elected a new standards watchdog.' *6 December*

As part of the largest ever recruitment drive to bolster Britain's flagging police force, Home Secretary David Blunkett lifted the 170-year ban on employing foreign nationals in its ranks.

'Will you tell him or shall I about what we normally do with speedsters?'   *7 December*

The £20,000 Turner Prize for art was won by 33-year-old Martin Creed from Wakefield, Yorkshire, with his installation 'The Lights Going On and Off', featuring an empty room in which the lights go on and off every five seconds.

'You're going to have to pull your socks up, Robinson. Look at the work Jenkins is producing – and he's younger than you.' *11 December*

A government report commissioned after last year's race riots in the North of England recommended that immigrants should learn English and take an oath of allegiance to the Queen. Meanwhile, a survey revealed an increase in excessive drinking among women.

'Don't worry. She's just trying to be more English.' *13 December*

A new European treaty agreed that any European country could extradite anyone making xenophobic remarks about their country and try them in their own courts. Meanwhile, the 12 British planespotters arrested in Greece were released on bail after a long campaign by the *Daily Mail*.

'I'm sorry, he can't talk right now. He's being extradited to Greece.' *14 December*

As US-led forces bombed the Taliban's last remaining stronghold in the Tora Bora caves in southern Afghanistan there was still no sign of Osama Bin Laden, who was later believed by many to have been smuggled into neighbouring Pakistan.

'I bet he's shaved off his beard and slipped into Pakistan or somewhere that's easy to get into.' *17 December*

The Police Federation threatened industrial action over Home Secretary David Blunkett's plans to reform the police force, which included the introduction of patrolling 'Civilian Support Officers' to combat Britain's escalating street crime.

'I don't care if they are the new civilian police support officers, Blunkett. I want my policemen back!' *18 December*

The 68-year-old actress Joan Collins announced her engagement to 36-year-old Peruvian-born theatre director Percy Gibson.

'Hi. I'm Betty from Accounts. Single, same age as Joan Collins and what are you doing this weekend?' *20 December*

As a big freeze welcomed in the New Year, 12 European countries – Austria, Belgium, Finland, France, Ireland, Italy, Germany, Greece, Holland, Luxembourg, Portugal and Spain – abandoned their centuries-old currencies in favour of the euro.

'Let's try again. A packet of peppermints is 50p. He gave us one euro. So that's 64 divided by . . .'   *3 January 2002*

Scientists working for the company that helped create Dolly the sheep at Edinburgh's Roslin Institute in 1996 announced that they had cloned five piglets which had been genetically engineered as 'organ factories' for human transplant surgery.

'Women! Can anyone understand them? I finally do something about my snoring and she leaves home.'   *4 January*

Rail commuters already suffering from dismal services – compounded by a series of regional strikes by the Rail, Maritime and Transport Union – were incensed when train operators announced the introduction of huge fare rises on hundreds of routes.

'I hope you weren't thinking of travelling with that ticket you bought three hours ago, squire. The fares have just gone up.' *7 January*

In the latest in a series of disclosures by junior members of the Royal Family, a new biography of the Queen by journalist Graham Turner alleged that there had been deep rifts between the Prince of Wales and his parents.

'You heard your father! All you have to do is tell the newspapers what wonderful parents you have and you're free.'
10 January

As train services continued to deteriorate and rail unions threatened to spread their strike action nationwide, Labour's Europe Minister Peter Hain, interviewed in the *Spectator* magazine, conceded that Britain now had 'the worst railways in Europe'.

'We did it, folks. We finally did it! – worst in Europe!' *11 January*

Prince Charles sent 17-year-old Prince Harry to a drug rehabilitation centre in south London after the *News of the World* revealed that he had admitted to under-age drinking and smoking cannabis.

'Prince Charles has had them placed all around the house as a warning to Harry.' *14 January*

Faced with growing disquiet from commuters, Prime Minister Tony Blair reported that the Strategic Rail Authority would spend £33.5 million of taxpayers' money over the next ten years in an effort to return the railways to acceptable standards of service.

'Good news, everybody. Only nine years, eleven months, twenty-nine days, six hours and thirty-five minutes to go . . .' *15 January*

The US was widely condemned for not treating Afghan prisoners of war held in a camp in Cuba according to the Geneva Convention. Meanwhile, a transatlantic version of Anne Robinson's *The Weakest Link* TV quiz show was shown in the US.

'This part is the worst bit apparently – who exactly is Anne Robinson?' *21 January*

'What a view, eh, Martin? From here you can see where Airey Neave was killed, the Old Bailey bomb site, the Hyde Park nail-bomb site, the . . .' *22 January*

A jury at Guildford Crown Court in Surrey heard that a 26-year-old biology mistress in a local comprehensive school had allegedly had sex with three teenage boys aged between 14 and 15 within weeks of her appointment as a supply teacher.

'Miss Frobisher, would you mind doing your top button up? Some of the parents are worrying.' *24 January*

The National Health Service came under attack when it was reported that a 94-year-old accident victim admitted to a London hospital had spent two-and-a-half days in a corridor waiting for a bed, unwashed and wearing the same clothes she arrived in.

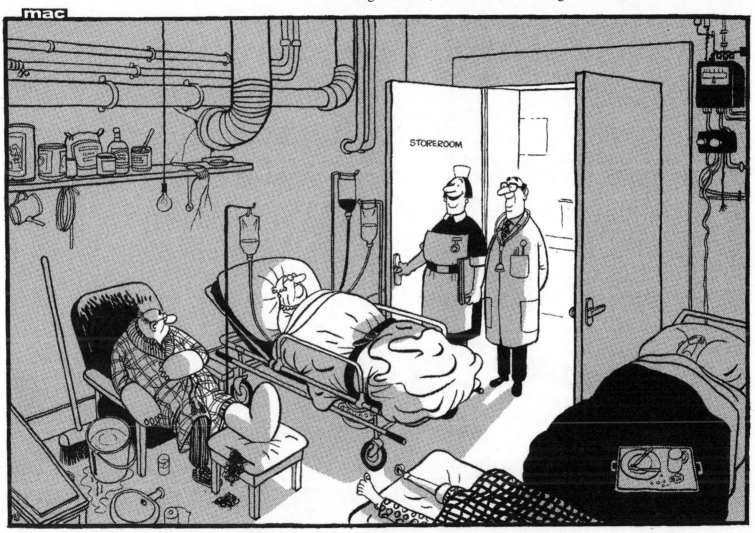

'Good news, everybody! We're planning a hanging-around-unwashed-in-a-corridor party to celebrate the Queen's Golden Jubilee.' *28 January*

The management of South West Trains warned 2,500 striking union-led rail-workers to stop their industrial action or risk losing their jobs to non-union replacements.

'Ah, here comes Marjorie. I asked her to pop in for a cuppa and a chat about her new job.' *29 January*

As NHS waiting lists continued to grow, it was revealed that a vet in Cheshire had performed a successful operation to cure a painful hip on a three-year-old labrador dog. The operation, costing £10,000, was covered by a pet insurance policy.

'I wonder if that vet's ever considered doing work for the NHS.' *1 February*

In an effort to ease the burden of Britain's overcrowded jails, Home Secretary David Blunkett announced plans for a new system in which electronically tagged offenders were locked up at night and at weekends but were released in the daytime to work.

'Great news, sir. I'm only locked up at nights and weekends now for my violent behaviour. So Mr Blunkett says I can keep my job.' *4 February*

Only months after being forced to sell off its cut-price subsidiary Go and the collapse of a proposed transatlantic partnership with American Airlines, British Airways announced that it was to cut 16,000 jobs in an attempt to stem huge losses of £6 billion.

'Honeshtly, folks. You try your best, work your shocks off, then in mid-air how do the b******s repay you?' *5 February*

Prime Minister Tony Blair was accused of 'designer diplomacy' and ignoring his own domestic problems when he arrived in Nigeria for a five-day tour of four West African countries, focussing on helping their ailing economies.

'Our problems are over! Tony Blair's here to save Africa.' *7 February*

Home Secretary David Blunkett's White Paper on immigrants introduced the Highly Skilled Migrant Programme in which applicants for British citizenship would have to pass exams in spoken and written English and swear to observe the country's laws.

'They f****** shouldn't be allowed in the f****** country if they can't f****** well speak f****** English properly!' *8 February*

Tory leader Iain Duncan Smith continued to search for new ways to improve his party's image. Meanwhile, 9 million telephone votes – the largest in the history of British TV – were received from viewers during the final of the hugely successful *Pop Idol* TV series.

'Apparently Iain Duncan Smith has come up with a great idea on how to defeat voter apathy at the next election.' *11 February*

There were more accusations of sleaze when it was reported that Tony Blair had personally supported a bid by Indian billionaire Lakshmi Mittal over a Romanian steel deal only weeks after Mittal had donated £125,000 to the Labour Party.

'Hello. Another tour. There must be some more sleaze at home.'   *12 February*

The nation celebrated St Valentine's Day on 14 February.

'Sorry this is late, love. Industrial dispute. I expect you thought you weren't going to get a Valentine card.' *15 February*

There was growing concern as figures published by pensions watchdog OPRA (the Occupational Pensions Regulatory Authority) revealed that one in three company pension schemes had been scrapped by employers in the last decade.

'As a token of our appreciation, Charlie, please accept this clock which was bought with what remained of your pension.' *21 February*

According to the *New Scientist* a new condition, Irritable Male Syndrome, has been officially recognised in middle-aged men. Triggered by stress and a sudden drop in testosterone levels, it can be treated with Hormone Replacement Therapy.

'You can get dressed now, Mr Gribley. I've had a look at my notes and I think you may have Irritable Male Syndrome.' *1 March*

The first clinically proven anti-baldness pills were launched in Britain. Available only on private prescription, the drug, Propecia, allegedly not only prevents hair loss in men but also promotes new growth. However, reported side-effects include loss of libido.

'They're working, Mary! The baldness cure pills are working!'   *5 March*

In an attempt to recruit more soldiers, new British Army regulations were introduced to allow spouses and partners of serving military personnel to stay overnight in army bases.

'Late again, you 'orrible little woman! Report in romantic mood to my sleeping quarters at the double! **LEFT, RIGHT, LEFT, RIGHT . . .**' *7 March*

As a counter-measure in the battle against soaring street crime, especially that involving guns and knives, Home Secretary David Blunkett unveiled plans to increase police powers to stop and search suspects for illegal weapons.

'When do we do the *un*desirables, sarge?' *11 March*

The government was accused of breaking its promises to abolish mixed-sex wards in 95% of NHS hospitals at the end of 2002 when Health Minister Hazel Blears announced that some could remain if permanent screens were erected between beds.

'Take my word for it. Your hernia is never going to get better if you're up all night bricking poor Mr Wilmott in.' *14 March*

'Paperwork? I never complain about all the paperwork – shall I roll another joint for you too, sweetie?' *18 March*

After finally admitting that ever-increasing street crime had made Britain's cities unsafe, Home Secretary David Blunkett introduced a six-month Robbery Reduction Initiative in which 5,000 police officers would be transferred back on to the beat.

'Of course, it takes a bit longer to get to the shops but at least you don't get mugged.' *19 March*

As street-crime figures in Britain reached a new high, Rural Affairs Minister Alun Michael announced that though stag-hunting and hare-coursing would be banned, fox-hunting with dogs would be allowed to continue as a means of pest control only.

'Makes you laugh, don't it? How do that bunch of plonkers in the government think they're goin' to reduce street crime?' *21 March*

New Home Office plans to combat crime included fixed-penalty on-the-spot fines for loutish behaviour. It was also announced that, to ease Britain's overcrowded prisons, thousands of offenders would be tagged and released early from jail.

'Blunkett's getting tougher. Normally the tags are fixed around the ankle.' *22 March*

After Culture Secretary Tessa Jowell introduced a White Paper proposing a relaxation on casino-licensing and gambling – thereby earning the government £1.5 billion a year in tax – developers planned to make Blackpool the gambling capital of Europe.

'Tell y'what. Let's have one more go at this daft kid's game then all pop next door for bingo and a bacon buttie.' *28 March*

The collapse of ITV Digital, after last-minute attempts to renegotiate its crippling £315-million contract with the Football League, spelled doom to many small clubs which relied on income from television-coverage sales to stay afloat.

'I know reading isn't one of your strong points, Wayne. So I'm afraid I've got to tell you some rather bad news . . .' *29 March*

Her Majesty, Queen Elizabeth the Queen Mother, widow of King George VI and famous for her love of horse-racing, died peacefully in her sleep at the Royal Lodge, Windsor, on Saturday 30 March 2002, aged 101.

CLEAR WINNER *1 April*

House prices – which had already risen by nearly 40% since 1999 – continued to rocket in 2002, confounding predictions by building societies that the boom was nearly at an end.

'Darling, it's that nice young couple who rang this morning when the house was £20,000 cheaper.'   *5 April*

There were fears for passenger safety when a major computer glitch at the National Air Traffic Control System – the second within two weeks – caused widespread chaos and the delay or cancellation of 700 UK flights affecting 150,000 air travellers.

'We apologise to passengers for the severe delays. Rest assured our engineers are working flat out to trace the computer fault . . .' *11 April*

Angry motorists felt they were being seen as soft targets as police forces nationwide flocked to join the government's new National Safety Camera Initiative which allows them to keep part of the income from speeding fines.

'Never mind the rapes and muggings. How much have our speed cameras made for us this week?' *12 April*

The Flora London Marathon was won by American Khalid Khannouchi, who finished in 2 hours 5 minutes 38 seconds. Britain's Paula Radcliffe won the women's race. In Augusta, Georgia, Tiger Woods won the US Masters golf tournament.

'Where've you been? No lunch yesterday. No supper. Then last night some idiot kept ringing the doorbell all through the Masters golf coverage.' *15 April*

In her memoirs, *Momentum*, former Northern Ireland Secretary Mo Mowlam spoke of a rift between the Prime Minister and Chancellor Gordon Brown, and accused Labour Party colleagues of 'vicious, violent and horrible' behaviour towards her while she was in office.

'It's probably Mo Mowlam.' *16 April*

In his Budget, Chancellor Gordon Brown announced the biggest increase in public spending in 30 years. Meanwhile, new detention laws for 12- to 16-year-olds were introduced to combat soaring street crime.

'You'll be lucky. Gordon Brown got here first.' *18 April*

Following the publication of a Treasury report on the NHS by Derek Wanless, it was revealed that the main beneficiary of the Chancellor's spending spree would be the Health Service, which would receive billions of pounds a year in extra funding.

'Right, team. One more toasht to Gordon Brown, then out with thish young lady's appendix – or is it bresht implants we're doing?' *19 April*

Only weeks before the World Cup began, England's football captain, David Beckham, broke a bone in his left foot and 53-year-old team manager Sven Goran Ericksson admitted to an affair with fellow Swede Ulrika Jonsson, a 34-year-old TV presenter.

'You naughty boy, Sven. When you get that misty-eyed look, I know exactly what you've got in mind . . .' *22 April*

The *International Journal of Impotence Research* reported that a new pill had been developed in Germany that could boost male sexual stamina and that promised to be even more popular than the anti-impotence drug Viagra.

'Cooeee, darling. Where are you? Time for our attempt at the world record . . .' *25 April*

In what was seen by many as a travesty of British justice, two teenage brothers accused of the murder of ten-year-old Damilola Taylor in London in 2000 were acquitted through lack of evidence after a three-month trial costing £7 million.

26 April

A 27-year-old male streaker from North Shields, with 'Rude Britannia' tattooed on his buttocks, ran beside the Queen's car for 50 yards as she drove to St Mary's Cathedral, Newcastle upon Tyne, to unveil a statue in honour of the late Cardinal Basil Hume.

'There was a streaker? Goodness me, I must be getting old. I didn't notice.' *9 May*

It was reported that legal-aid bills for asylum-seekers had doubled over the last ten years, turning this into a boom industry for lawyers. Some unscrupulous law firms even sent touts to Britain's air- and seaports to target immigrants as they arrived.

'Please go away. I keep telling you I don't want to sneak into Britain and make use of your legal advice!' *10 May*

In another 'cash-for-favours' scandal, it was revealed that media baron Richard Desmond had made a donation of £100,000 to the Labour Party just days before the government cleared his company, Northern & Shell, to take over the Express Group.

'I know it's hard, Mr Blair. But if you can curb your craving for donations the arm will soon straighten out.' *13 May*

No legal action was taken after a rail disaster at Potters Bar station, in which seven people were killed, was blamed on faulty track maintenance. Meanwhile, a diver was imprisoned for six months for retrieving 1,158 golf balls from a lake at a golf club in Leicestershire.

News Item: **A Man was Jailed Recently for Taking Golf Balls from a Lake** *14 May*

Relatives of a 43-year-old British woman who had told her family she worked in market research were stunned when she was arrested in Paris and charged with running France's biggest vice ring, involving 450 girls charging up to £600 an hour.

'The amazing thing is, Doris, none of the relatives had a clue what she was up to . . .'   *17 May*

The *News of the World* reported that 45-year-old Angus Deayton, host of BBC TV's satirical panel game *Have I Got News for You*, co-starring Ian Hislop and Paul Merton, had had sex and snorted cocaine through a £20 note with an escort girl.

'Well, I'm the producer and I want Paul Merton and Ian Hislop back!' *21 May*

A Commons Home Affairs Committee Report on drugs that recommended the downgrading of the categorisations of ecstasy and cannabis, and the legal penalties for their possession, was seen by many to be sending out the 'wrong message'.

'"Britons, never, never, never, shall be slaves . . ."' *23 May*

A leaked report revealed that staff at the new £623-million air traffic control centre at Swanwick had difficulty reading letters and numbers on their computer screens and that in one case a plane bound for Glasgow had been accidentally routed to Cardiff.

'Gee, Hank. I'm new to this route. What do the people of Cardiff look like?' *24 May*

As two hostile neighbours, India and Pakistan, threatened a nuclear holocaust over Kashmir, the focus of British media attention was on whether England skipper David Beckham's injured foot would heal in time for the start of the 2002 World Cup.

'Have you got anything on the India–Pakistan nuclear threat?' *28 May*

Disgraced Transport Minister Stephen Byers finally resigned after months of criticism and allegations that he had lied to Parliament. His successor in the troubled ministry was former Work & Pensions Secretary Alistair Darling.

'. . . Now come along. Get off that window ledge. Of course life's worth living . . . oh, please don't cry, Mr Darling . . .' *30 May*

Japanese police revealed their plans to deal with football hooligans as British fans arrived for England's opening match against Sweden in the World Cup. Meanwhile, the Home Office announced that it would deport 30,000 failed asylum-seekers.

'Another lot claiming to be illegal immigrants who ought to be deported to Japan immediately.' *31 May*

The celebrations to mark the Queen's Golden Jubilee included classical and pop music concerts at Buckingham Palace. Among those performing in the pop concert were Sir Cliff Richard, Sir Elton John and Tom Jones.

'Do stop fidgeting, Philip. I'm told it will be expected of one to throw undergarments at Tom Jones when he sings tonight.' *3 June*

Following the pop concert, attended by 12,000 people with a million more outside watching on giant screens, the final day of the Jubilee celebrations included a ceremonial procession from Buckingham Palace to St Paul's Cathedral.

'Only nine hours, thirty-five minutes and eleven seconds to go . . .' *4 June*

There was fury from motorists in London when a company employing 320 parking wardens in the Borough of Westminster announced that it would give bonuses of up to £1,200 as an incentive to wardens to issue more parking tickets.

'Aw, isn't it a shame? Just picked up his bonus when he got mugged by a gang of motorists.' *6 June*

The 59-year-old lead singer of the Rolling Stones, Mick Jagger – as famous for his hedonistic lifestyle as for his music – was knighted in the Queen's Birthday Honours on the personal recommendation of Prime Minister Tony Blair.

'Mick's so pleased, he's making a donation to the Labour Party – us!' *11 June*

Downing Street dismissed claims that officials at No. 10 had tried to engineer a bigger role for Tony Blair at the Queen Mother's Lying in State in Westminster Hall, during which her four grandchildren had stood sentinel at each corner of her coffin.

'A bit late, but the Prime Minister's still determined to take a bigger part in the Queen Mother's funeral.' *13 June*

As accommodation for asylum-seekers became an issue, an official report into royal finances criticised Prince Michael of Kent, who has no royal duties, for retaining a seven-bedroom grace-and-favour apartment in Kensington Palace at the taxpayer's expense, as well as a 16th-century mansion in Gloucestershire.

'Well, I think you should have consulted me before you reached a compromise with Blair.' *14 June*

In the World Cup in Japan, England beat Denmark 3–0 to go through to the quarter-finals for the first time in 12 years. Meanwhile, England's cricket team played Sri Lanka in the Third Test at Old Trafford, Manchester.

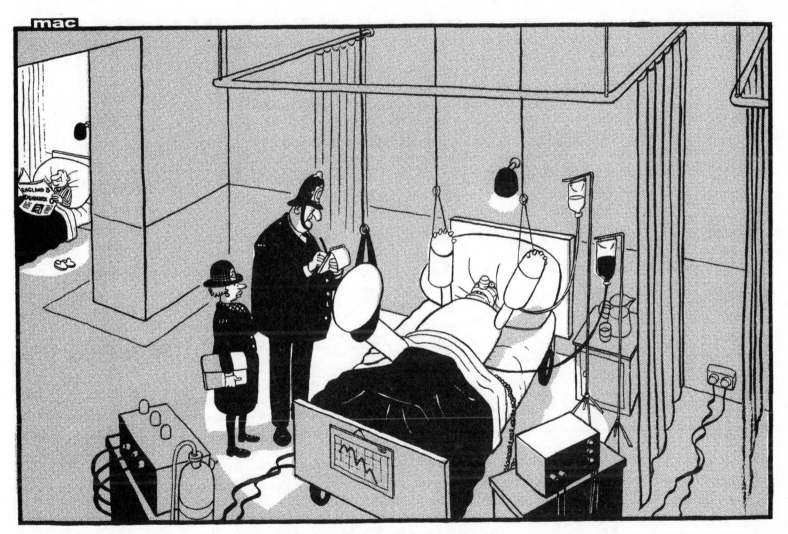

'I see, sir. You were in this crowded pub on Saturday and you switched the TV over to watch the test match against Sri Lanka . . . What happened next?' *17 June*

The Prime Minister's wife, Cherie Blair, sparked a diplomatic row when she appeared to sympathise with Palestinian suicide-bombers in a speech made at the launch of a charity appeal on the day when a bus was blown up in Jerusalem, killing 19 Israelis.

'Hello. Looks like there's been another reshuffle.' *20 June*

Despite the time difference between Japan and the UK – which meant that the quarter-final match between England and Brazil in the World Cup was broadcast early in the morning – 30 million British viewers tuned in. In the event Brazil won 2–1.

'You were sleeping so soundly we didn't want to wake you – do you want to know the score?' *21 June*

Only months after the Enron accounting scandal, the US telecommunications company World Com was at the centre of the biggest corporate fraud in history, sending stock markets crashing. Meanwhile, Britain's Tim Henman reached the second round of Wimbledon.

'It must be pretty serious. Don't tell me Tim Henman's been beaten!' *27 June*

Scientists at the US Department of Agriculture discovered that caffeine is a deadly deterrent to slugs and snails.

'Okay. They're on the cheese and biscuits now – go hit them with the coffee!' *28 June*

Brazil won the 2002 World Cup by beating Germany 2–0 in Yokohama, Japan.

'The World Cup is finally over? Okay, darling. I'll just help mother wash up and catch the next train home.' *1 July*

Home Secretary David Blunkett introduced a White Paper on the subject of the issuing of identity cards in Britain based on the European model, to help in the battle against illegal immigration and welfare-benefit fraud.

'Excuse me, if you're Arabella Pilkington-Smythe, formerly Arthur Finkley, who's £435.20 in the red, been married three times and has two moles on her right buttock – you've dropped your ID card.' *2 July*

A £50,000 marble statue of former Prime Minister Margaret Thatcher, which had been specially commissioned by the House of Commons and only unveiled in May, was decapitated by a vandal at the Guildhall Art Gallery, London.

'Courage, lad – you won't feel a thing.'   *5 July*

The all-party House of Commons Public Accounts Committee proposed scrapping the Royal Train – which costs taxpayers £703,000 a year and was used for only 15 journeys in 2001 – thereby ending 160 years of privileged rail travel for the monarchy.

'Now what has New Labour done? First they scrap Britannia, then the Royal Train . . .' *8 July*

As Royal Mail announced that customers receiving fewer than 20 items a day would be charged £14 a week for deliveries before 9am, a government report recommended charging £1 per sack to dispose of household waste, to encourage recycling.

'Most of this early post for which we pay £14 a week is rubbish for which we pay £1 a bag to get rid of.' *12 July*

Though Home Secretary David Blunkett's new relaxed laws on the use and possession of cannabis were not due to come into effect until 2003, police forces nationwide seemed already to be turning a blind eye as many people began openly to smoke pot in public parks.

15 July

Chancellor Gordon Brown put schools and colleges at the centre of a huge public-spending spree which included the promise of direct payments worth up to £50,000 to every comprehensive school in England for each of the next three years.

'You're a very lucky boy, Wilkins. With everybody else playing truant and smoking pot in the park, guess how much the Chancellor is spending on you?' *16 July*

A strike of 750,000 council workers paralysed public services as members of the Unison, TGWU and GMB unions demanded higher wages. Meanwhile, the 2002 Open Golf championship began in Muirfield.

'I'm ringing about your boss, Mr Grimbly. That's right, the chap who called you council workers a bunch of lazy, strike-crazy b******s – he's fallen seriously ill for three days.' *18 July*

Deputy Prime Minister John 'Two Jaguars' Prescott announced plans to build more than 800,000 new homes in the south of England over the next 15 years, fuelling fears from rural communities that London's Green Belt areas would soon be concreted over.

'You're the only Archer left, Phil. The family have emigrated, the farm's a building site . . . look out, Phil! Mind that bulldozer! . . . Oh no! . . . Dumpty dumpty dumpty dum . . .' *19 July*

A government report recommended fitting satellite-trackable microchips in cars so that motorists could be charged for road use and traffic congestion could be monitored. Civil liberties groups dubbed it the 'spy in the car' scheme.

'It'll be terrible if the government's "spy in the car" scheme is approved. My wife would be the first to check up where I'd been.'
22 July

Official statistics revealed that Britain had the worst teenage pregnancy rates in Europe, with 400 girls aged under 14 giving birth every year. Meanwhile, Virgin Trains received £465 million in compensation for delays to track upgrading which prevented it running its new 140mph tilting trains.

'There, I told you we should have waited!' *23 July*

There was public anger when it was reported that asylum-seekers – many of whom would be eventually deported – had enjoyed camping holidays, swimming galas and visits to the theatre, Madame Tussauds and the Tower of London, all at the taxpayer's expense.

'Aren't the British wonderful? First a visit to the Tower, then Madame Tussaud's, and now a mystery trip.' *25 July*

Less than a week after another serious near-miss in Britain's crowded skies, two passenger jets carrying 152 people were reported to have been within six seconds of a collision.

'Don't worry, everyone. It was only a slight knock. The captain is just exchanging insurance details . . .' *26 July*

While on holiday in the US, Tory Party Chairman David Davis was given the sack by Iain Duncan Smith. His new job was to shadow Labour's Deputy Prime Minister John Prescott.

'**John, dear. When does this Davis bloke start his new job?**' *29 July*

In what was seen as the first test of his party's new commitment to tolerance, Tory front-bench spokesman on foreign affairs, Alan Duncan, became the first Conservative MP ever to openly declare himself to be gay.

'I don't know about you chaps, but I'm surprised. I can usually spot one a mile off.' *30 July*

Despite receiving massive new funding, the crisis in the NHS continued. Lacking ambulances, the fire brigade was sent to treat a case in Yorkshire, and a Southend man suffering from burns was driven 250 miles to Swansea to find a bed in a specialist unit.

'Sorry, there are no beds available on this floor either – have you tried Swansea?'   *1 August*

A report in the *New Scientist* revealed that a joint study by researchers at the University of Lincoln and the University of Minas Gerais in Brazil had shown that dogs can count and that their barking is more like a language than previously supposed.

'Don't look like that. I've only had two pints.'   *2 August*

A report by the government 'think tank' Migration Watch revealed that immigrants entering Britain had now reached a record 250,000 a year – enough to fill a city the size of Cambridge every six months. A large proportion came from eastern Europe.

'If you want totally empty beaches and uncrowded cities, try Albania or Romania – they're all over here!' *6 August*

In what was seen as a travesty of justice when burglaries, muggings and other crimes go almost unheeded, several police officers arrived rapidly and a Norfolk couple were imprisoned for 28 days after cutting down a boundary hedge between their home and a neighbour's.

'It's a fair cop – as well as next door's privet hedge I'd like a rose bush and a rather unruly heliotrope to be taken into consideration.' *8 August*

A study by a French cardiologist revealed that long-distance drivers are as much at risk from deep vein thrombosis (DVT) as air passengers. Meanwhile, a sudden deluge brought chaos to the capital when two-thirds of London's average monthly rainfall was delivered in 30 minutes.

'Careful, officer. I think you may be standing on my husband. He's doing some press-ups.' *9 August*

There was a storm of protest when it was revealed that the National Lottery's Community Fund had agreed to donate £340,000 of lottery-players' money to charities set up to help asylum-seekers.

'Okay, you illegal immigrants, we know you're in there. Come out and get what's coming to you!'   *13 August*

As A-level results hit a new high with a pass-rate of 94.3% and predictions of a 100% pass-rate by 2004, many employers and universities argued that the examinations were getting easier and that they were no longer a useful measure of ability.

'90 per cent of me wants to go out and celebrate, but the other 50 per cent asks: Were they dumbing down?' *15 August*

More than one hundred prominent atheists demanded a voice on the 'Thought for the Day' religious slot on BBC Radio 4's 'Today' programme hosted by John Humphrys.

'Look, if he insists on his right to do "Thought for the Day", who's arguing?' *16 August*

After a huge media campaign, a man and a woman were arrested and charged in connection with the killing of two ten-year-old schoolgirls – Holly Wells and Jessica Chapman – from Soham, Cambridgeshire.

BRITISH JUSTICE 2002

FOR PAEDOPHILIA & MURDER

PUNISHMENT EXPECTED

PUNISHMENT DESERVED

19 August

Disgraced multi-millionaire novelist and former Tory Party Chairman Jeffrey Archer was allowed out of prison on a day-release scheme to take up a £60-a-week job at the Theatre Royal, Lincoln, after serving 12 months of a four-year sentence for perjury.

'When you said "Your place or mine after the show?" I thought you had a posh house somewhere.' *20 August*

Britain's long diplomatic silence over the enforced evictions of white farmers in Zimbabwe was finally broken after the US publicly condemned the practice and declared that it did not recognise President Robert Mugabe as the country's legitimate leader.

'Oh. Er . . . right then. I condemn Mugabe too!' *23 August*

It was revealed that almost £18 million of National Lottery money had been spent helping asylum-seekers in Britain last year. Meanwhile, at the United Nations' 'Earth Summit' in Johannesburg, South Africa, delegates addressed the problem of world poverty.

'All in favour then? We send our poor, hungry and deprived to Britain where they'll get a lottery grant . . .' *27 August*

Despite negative opinion polls at home, and increasing international isolation, Tony Blair continued to back US President Bush's plan to make a pre-emptive attack on Iraq and its leader Saddam Hussein, in a bid to combat world terrorism.

'Aw, c'mon somebody. Ah cain't fight till ah gits me another glove.' *29 August*

Tension heightened as Bush and Blair continued to press for war with Iraq. Meanwhile, members of the RAF's 23 Squadron based at Waddington, Lincolnshire, posed naked for a charity calendar.

'We'll have no problems with the RAF, Illustrious One. Look, they can't even afford uniforms.' *30 August*

'Romeo, Romeo. Wherefore art thou, Romeo? Tis me, yer dad, wiv flars for yer mum.' *2 September*

Britain was put on a war footing as Prime Minister Tony Blair flew to the US for talks on Iraq with President Bush. Meanwhile, a record number of asylum-seekers in Britain – predominantly from Iraq and Afghanistan – led to a huge backlog in the processing of applications.

'Don't worry. By the time they've processed our asylum applications the bombing will be over and we can go home.'

3 September